30 Maths GAMES
for Lower Primary

Catherine Connolly

Prim-Ed Publishing

Introduction

In recent years I have become enthusiastic about the role board games might play in the teaching of mathematics in the infant classroom. The Cockcroft Report Mathematics Counts 1971 states that 'all pupils need opportunities to practise skills and routines which have been acquired recently and to consolidate those which they already possess, so they may be available for use in problem solving and investigational work.'

Board games provide an opportunity for the practice of basic mathematical skills in a way that is enjoyable for the child. The variety of games allows the less able child much needed repetition. Games make this repetitive memorising interesting and reinforce lightly held knowledge. While playing games, children are relaxed and have a good learning disposition, and the element of chance inherent in the games allows the less able child to succeed.

Games aid in the development of:
- visual, motor and memory skills;
- social skills;
- language skills;
- left to right orientation recognition; and
- concentration and dexterity.

Games provide additional benefits.
- They provide excitement and challenge.
- They provide a happy and purposeful activity taken at the child's own pace, in which children are actively involved.
- Certain basic concepts are constantly reinforced in a variety of contexts.
- They encourage a positive attitude toward mathematics.
- They can be played individually or with a partner.
- They link in with existing mathematics schemes.
- They provide a guide to evaluation by the teacher.

 # Table of Contents

Basic Game-playing Rules

It is important to establish basic ground rules for playing games. These rules are best learnt initially in two player games. Praise children who play by the rules and treat other players fairly.

- Play depends on whatever symbol on the die lands uppermost.
- Wait for your turn to come and when it does, do not take several turns together.
- Play does not resume until the previous player has completed his/her turn.
- If a numeral or space is already covered, play passes to the next player.
- When play is complete, put the die back into the shaker and hand it to the next player.
- Accept reversals of fortune.

Using the Games

Where there is more than one game dealing with the same teaching point, start with a game you think the children would like, and over a period of time add to your collection. As your collection mounts up, rotate the games to retain childrens' interest. Games can be slotted into the timetable as one of the activities in the afternoon, or in the morning.

It is important the games be easily accessible to children so they can fetch and return them with as little adult help as possible. Praise children who put games away in an orderly manner. Store the game pieces in a plastic container. Paste a visual clue on the lid, or on the side if they are to be stacked. Encourage children to find the relevant container themselves.

Games are pictorial representations of the real thing, and it is presumed that a lot of concrete work will precede the use of these games e.g. talking about food, healthy eating, showing real items of food, fruit, discussion on colours, items of clothing etc. In relation to number work, nothing can replace working with concrete materials and working with the children themselves as a foundation for the important mathematical concepts of one-to-one correspondence, mapping and cardinal numbers. The purpose of the games in this book is to consolidate such foundation work, in an exciting and pleasurable way.

A class record can be kept for each term. Record each game that a child has played with a spot or a star. This encourages children to play a greater variety of games, and so benefit from their use.

Making the Games

1. Photocopy the game baseboard and pieces, enlarging if required.

2. Colour in the baseboard and game pieces with markers or paints, if required.

3. Paste the photocopied baseboard and pieces onto thick cardboard.

4. You may want to write or paste the games instructions on the back of the baseboard, for future reference.

5. Cover the front and back of the baseboard and game pieces with clear contact.

6. You can make up dice by marking or pasting symbols onto a wooden cube.

Game 1	Balloons	Pre-number

Aim: (i) To reinforce recognition of colours pink, yellow, blue, red, green and purple.
(ii) To give practice in matching.

What you need: One 'Balloons' baseboard per player.

Six balloon shapes per player backed with cardboard and coloured in the above colours. Use the 'Balloons' baseboard as a template for the balloon shapes.

A six-sided die featuring six colours: pink, yellow, blue, red, green and purple. Use a wooden cube coloured with marker pens.

No. of players: Two or three.

How to play: Each player takes a baseboard. They take turns to throw the die, putting a balloon on their baseboard according to the colour thrown. The winner is the first person to cover and match all of his/her balloons correctly. The game can be extended by playing it in reverse. This time the winner is the first player to remove all of his/her balloons from the baseboard.

Game 2	Slowcoach	Pre-number

Aim: To reinforce colour recognition (any six colours of your choice).

What you need: A 'Slowcoach' baseboard between two players. Colour the six squares on each track on the baseboard with six colours of your choice. Children prefer that the squares along both tracks are coloured in the same order, as they perceive this to be fairer.

Two counters to represent the positions of the two players. You can use the counters provided on the following page or make up your own; for example, real snail shells.

A six-sided die, featuring the six colours from the baseboard. Use a wooden cube coloured with marker pens.

No. of players: Two.

How to play: The baseboard can be played from left to right or from top to bottom. There are two tracks on the board made up of six coloured squares. Players choose the track they will play on. They take turns to throw the die. When the colour on the top face of the die after it has been thrown matches the coloured square on the track, they move along one space. They may have to wait several turns to move to the next space. The winner is the first player to reach the opposite end of the baseboard. The winner can also be the last player to reach the opposite end of the baseboard.

1

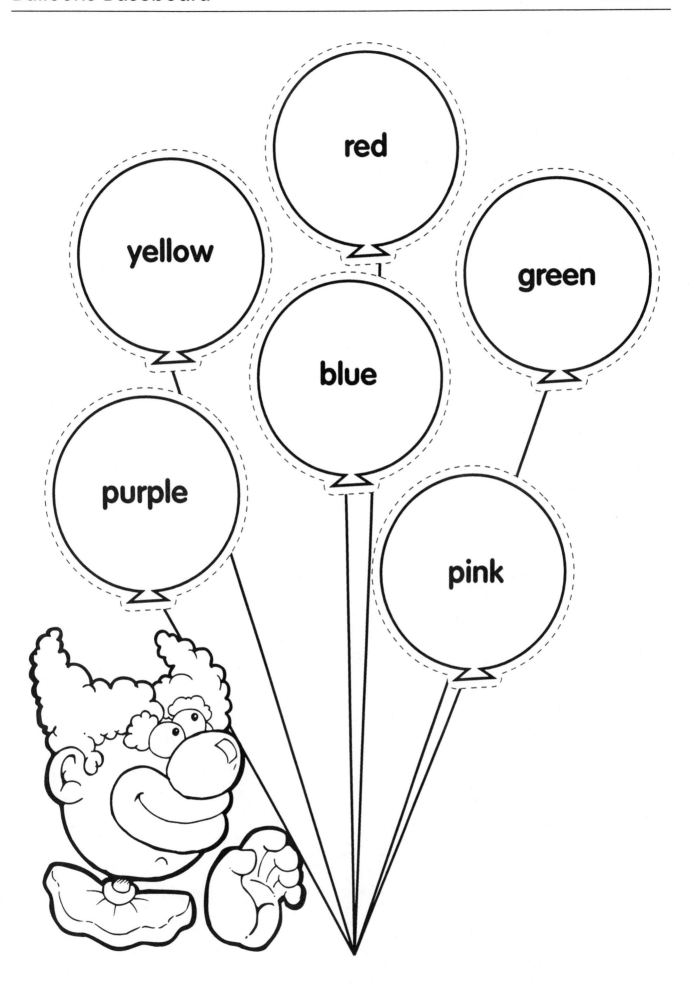

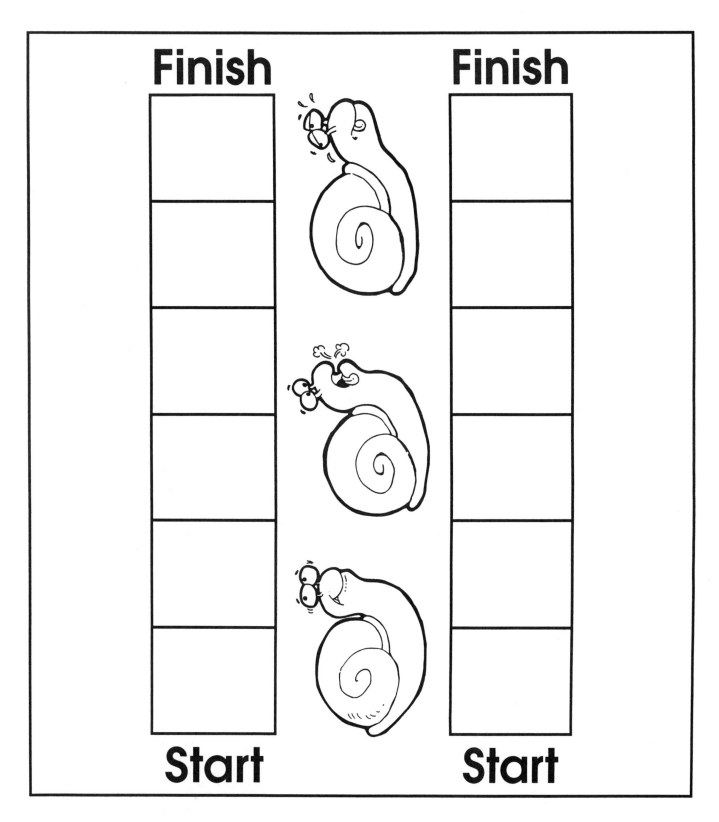

Game 3	Baby Bear's Bed	Pre-number

Aim: To reinforce colour recognition (any six colours of your choice).

What you need: A 'Baby Bear's Bed' baseboard for each player. The colours you have chosen are painted or pasted onto each baseboard. As there are twelve quilt patches on each baseboard, each colour is repeated twice per board, i.e. any one board will have two reds, two yellows, etc.

A set of twelve quilt patches in the six different colours for each player.

A six-sided die, featuring the six colours used on the baseboards. Use a wooden cube coloured with marker pens.

No. of players: Two or three.

How to play: Each player takes a baseboard and twelve patches (two sets of six different colours each). They take turns throwing the die and placing a patch according to the colour thrown. The first player to cover all the patches on the baseboard wins.

Play variation: This game can be played without using a die. Place the pile of patches face down between the players. They take it in turns to remove a patch from the top of the pile and place it on the corresponding patch on the bed. If there isn't any place for a patch on the baseboard, a new pile is started near the original pack. Again, the first player to cover all the patches on the baseboard is the winner.

Game 4	Humpty Dumpty	Pre-number

Aim: To reinforce visual discrimination and to give practice in matching.

What you need: Two baseboards. The baseboards supplied in this package come with designs already printed on them.

A pack of 24 cards which replicate the designs on the baseboards. You can cut these from the baseboard supplied.

Alternatively, you can customise your games by replacing the designs on the baseboard and cards with wallpaper from old sample books.

No. of players: Two.

How to play: Each player chooses a baseboard. The pile of pattern cards is placed face downwards between the players. Players take turns in removing a card from the top of the pile and placing it on their baseboard if it matches. If it does not match one of the design spaces on their baseboard, then a discard pile of cards is started next to the first pile. Once the players have been through the pile they shuffle the discard pile, place it face downwards and start again. The winner is the first player to cover all the spaces on their baseboard.

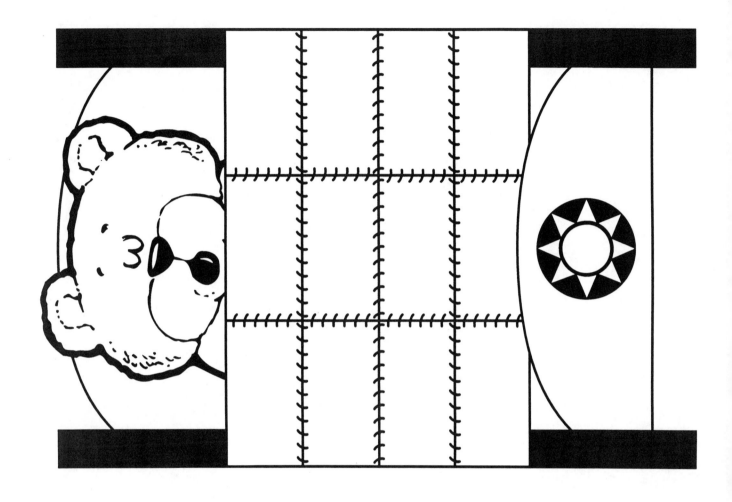

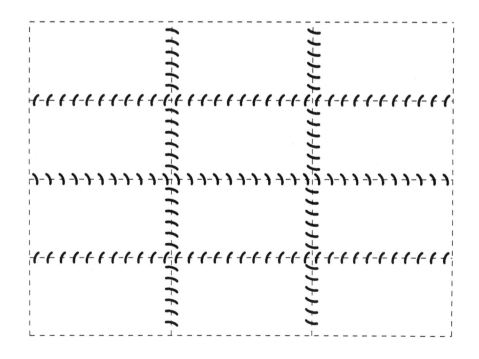

Game 5	**Coloured Lids**	**Pre-number**

Aim:

To reinforce colour recognition and memory skills.

What you need:

Tops from various aerosol cans. For example fly-killer, oven cleaner, furniture polish or deodorant cans. You will need purple, orange, pink, blue, green and yellow lids.

A six-sided die, featuring the colours of the six lids you have chosen. Use a wooden cube, coloured with marker pens.

No. of players:

This game can be played by two or three players, or it can be used by the teacher as a five minute filler with the class group.

How to play:

Find six items in the classroom, small enough to fit under the aerosol lids you have collected. For example, a building block, a bead or a cube. Hide these objects under the lids, letting the children see which object goes under which lid. Move the lids around for a few seconds. Appoint one child to throw the die. The child calls out the colour thrown. Ask the class 'Can anyone remember what is under the **x** lid'. If a child answers correctly, remove the lid from the game. Continue until all of the lids have been removed.

This game costs nothing to make and is quite enjoyable to play.

Game 6	**Lollipop**	**Pre-number**

Aim:

(i) To reinforce one-to-one correspondence and, incidentally, the cardinal aspect of numbers (1-5).
(ii) As a vocabulary exercise, giving a practical example of the words 'full', 'empty', 'inside', 'outside', etc.

What you need:

Two 'Lollipop' baseboards.

Five broad beans in a shaker with one side painted or coloured. Alternatively, you could use counters or coins with one side marked.

Twenty tops from two-litre plastic milk containers. You could paint these in several different colours to add visual appeal.

No. of players:

Two.

How to play:

Each player takes a baseboard. Players take turns to throw the beans, putting 'lollipops' in their jar according to the number of beans which land coloured side up. The game is over when all the spaces for the lollipops have been filled. The first player to do this is the winner. The game can also be played in reverse.

Play variation:

As the childrens' competence and familiarity with numbers increases you could introduce a bigger jar to hold twenty lollipops.

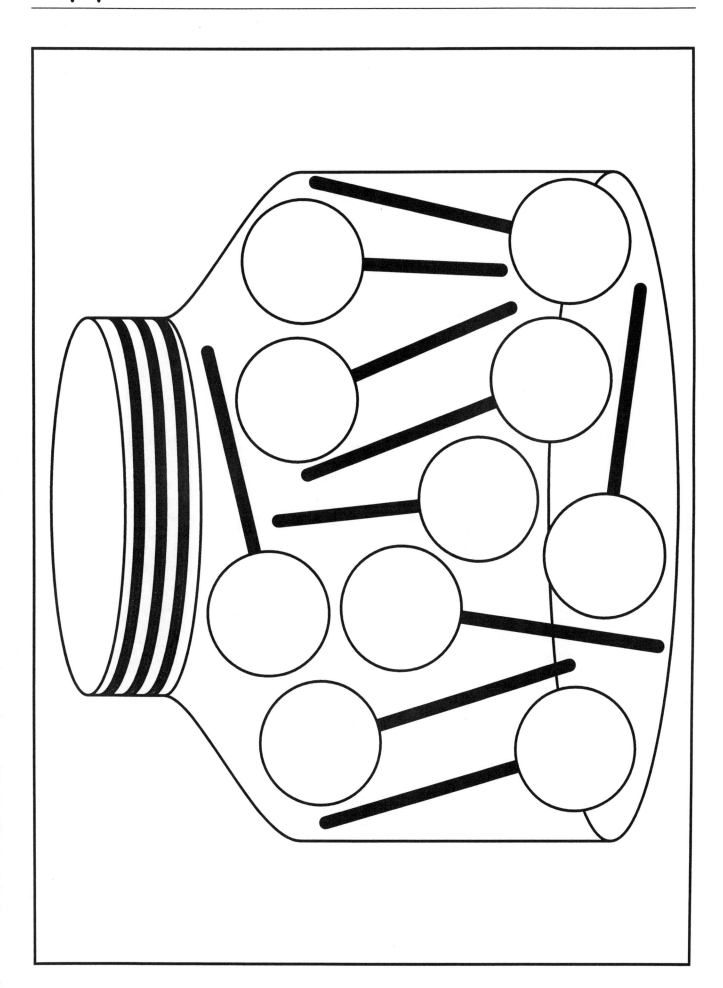

Game 7 — Clothesline

Pre-number

Aim:	(i) To reinforce left – right orientation. (ii) To follow a linear sequence in exact order.
What you need:	A 'Clothesline' baseboard for each player. Clothing counters corresponding to the clothing which appears on each baseboard. A six-sided die made from a wooden cube, featuring these items of clothing: t-shirt, shorts, skirt, trousers and socks. The sixth side of the die has a 'bonus' symbol – a washing machine. You can use the symbols provided below or draw your own.
No. of players:	Two.
How to play:	Starting at the far left side of the clothesline, players hang washing on the line according to the exact sequence on their baseboard. Players must wait for the first item of clothing on their baseboard to be rolled on the die before they can start. They may have to wait several turns to hang the next item of clothing on their baseboard. If the bonus symbol – the washing machine – is thrown by a player he or she can hang the next item of clothing on the line they need. The winner is the first person to hang all of their washing on the line. The game can be extended by playing it in reverse. This time the winner is the first player to take all of the washing off their clothesline.

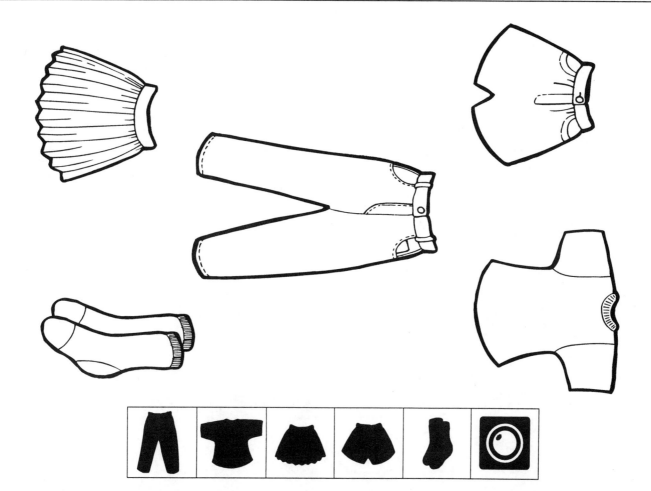

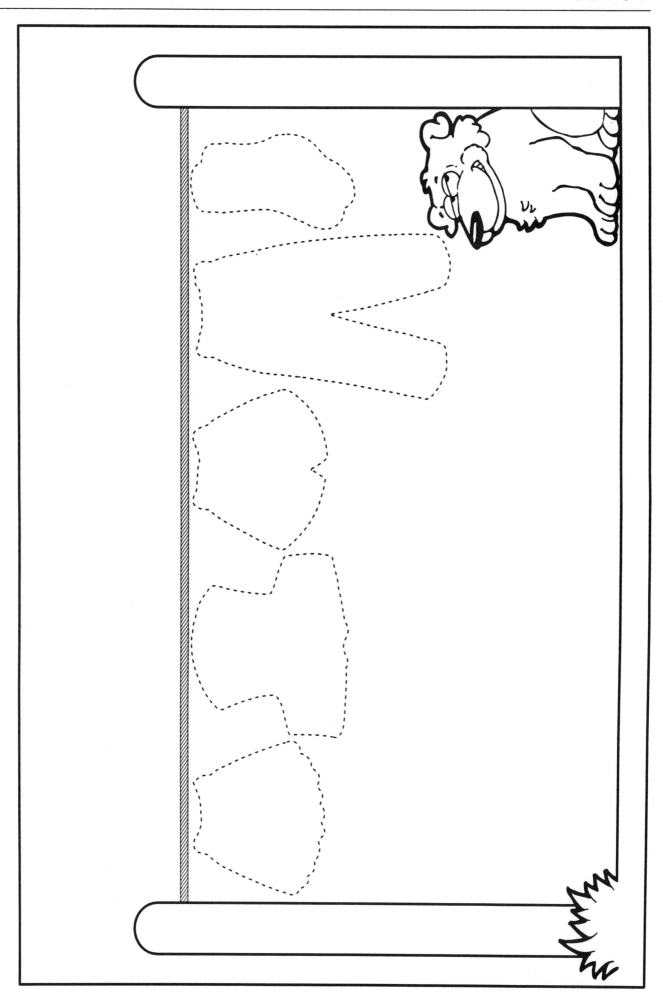

Game 8   Teddy Bear   Pre-number

Aim:
i) To reinforce the recognition and naming of basic body parts: eyes, ears, arms, legs, nose, mouth.
ii) To reinforce the concept of one-to-one correspondence.

What you need:
Two 'Teddy Bear' baseboards.

Two sets of teddy body parts (one set per baseboard).

A six-sided die showing the following symbols:

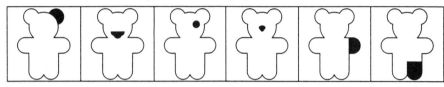

You can cut these out directly from a photocopy of this sheet and paste them onto a wooden cube.

No. of players:
Two.

How to play:
Players take it in turns to throw the die, putting the different body parts on their baseboard according to the throw of the die. The first player to complete his/her teddy is the winner. The game can be extended by playing it in reverse.

Game 9   Beehive   Pre-number

Aim:
i) To introduce the number line without the distraction of numerals.
ii) To reinforce left-to-right orientation.

What you need:
Five 'Flower' baseboards and a 'Beehive' baseboard between players. These boards fit together like jigsaw puzzle pieces.

Counters to mark the players progress. Bee counters are provided on the 'Beehive' baseboard.

Five broad beans in a shaker with one side painted or coloured. Alternatively, you could use counters or coins with one side marked.

No. of players:
Two or more.

How to play:
Each 'Flower' baseboard has four flowers standing in a row. The game can be played using two 'Flower' baseboards initially (8 flowers) and then extending to four or five 'Flower' baseboards (16 to 20 flowers) later.

The players place their bee counters on the flower at the extreme left of the first 'Flower' baseboard and progress towards the 'Beehive' baseboard, placed to the right of the last flower baseboard. Players take turns throwing the beans/counters and move their bee according to the number of beans that land coloured side up.

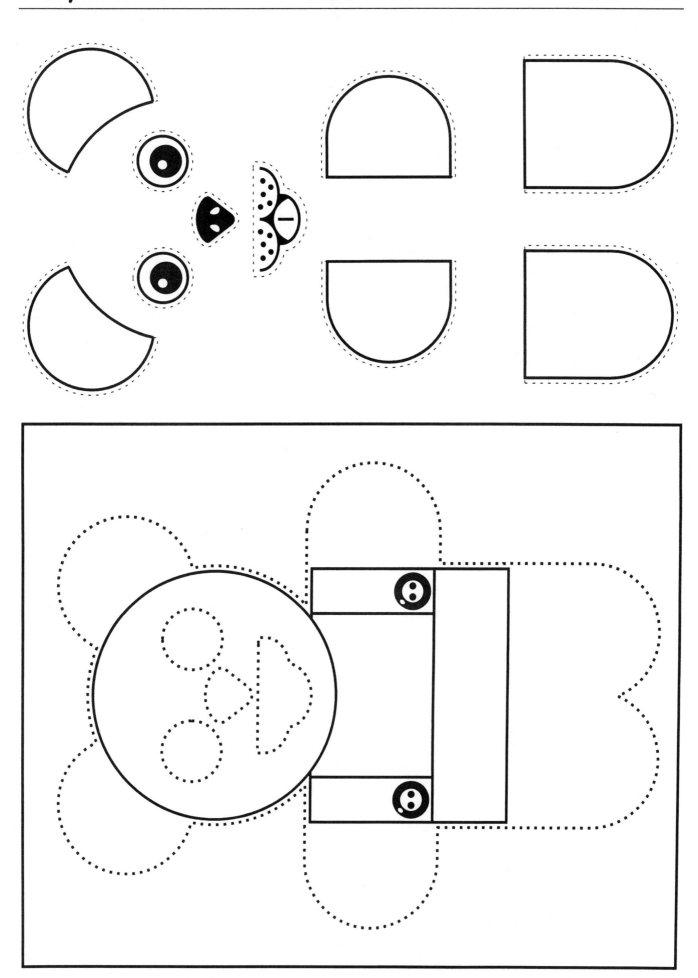

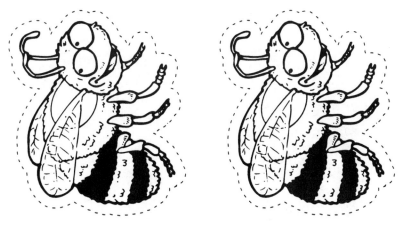

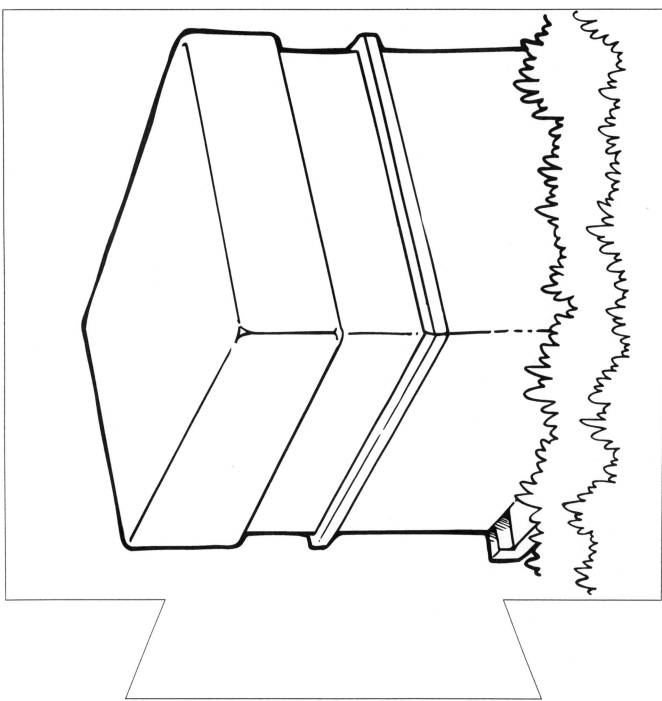

Game 10 · Lunchbox · Pre-number

Aim:
i) To give practice in matching.
ii) To promote healthy eating.

What you need:
Two 'Lunchbox' baseboards, each with the outlines of six items of food.

Six items of food to go in the lunchbox. You can use the game pieces provided. Alternatively, you could use wrappers from real foods – yoghurt cartons cut in half, drink cartons, wrappers from cheese triangles and snack bars. Back the wrappers on cardboard and cover them with clear contact.

A six-sided die, featuring the items of food in the lunchbox – a sandwich, yoghurt, drink, apple, piece of cheese and a treat. You can use the symbols below or draw these items yourself onto a wooden cube.

No. of players:
Two.

How to play:

Each player takes a baseboard and the six items of food that go with it. Players take turns throwing the die, putting the various game pieces on their baseboards, according to the throw of the die. The winner is the first player to fill his/her lunchbox. The game can be extended by playing it in reverse. Children particularly like this game when 'real life' wrappers and containers are used.

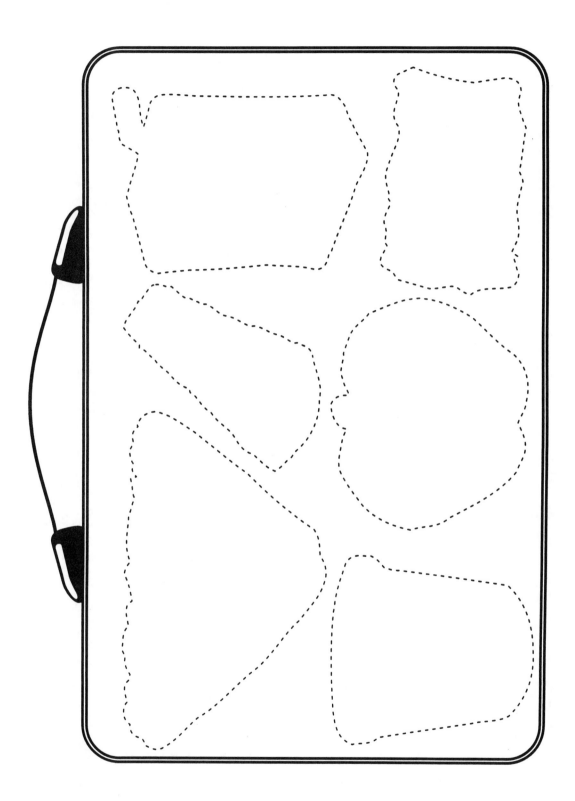

Game 11   Setting the Table   Pre-number

Aim:
    i)   To reinforce the concept of one-to-one correspondence.
    ii)   To promote language development on the topic of favourite food.

What you need:

A 'Setting the Table' baseboard for each player.

A cutlery set – knife, fork, spoon, drink and plate – for each player.

A food set featuring egg, chips, sausages, peas and beans. Alternatively, you could make up your own food set by using pictures from magazines or food wrappers. Paste these pictures to cardboard and mark their outlines onto their corresponding dinner plate.

A six-sided die, featuring the five items of the cutlery set and a bonus symbol. You can use the symbols below or draw these items yourself onto a wooden cube.

A six-sided die featuring the five items of food and a bonus symbol. You can use the symbols below or draw these items yourself onto a wooden cube.

No. of players: Two.

How to play:

Players each take a baseboard, a cutlery set and a food set. Play game 1 first and game 2 second.

Game 1:

Players take turns in throwing the cutlery die and putting their cutlery on their baseboard according to the item thrown. When the bonus symbol appears, the player may put any item needed on their baseboard. When a player has set their table they may start placing food.

Game 2:

As before, players take turns throwing the food die and placing their food onto their plate according to the item thrown. When the bonus symbol appears, the player may put any item on their plate.

The winner is the first player to set their table and serve up all of their food. The game can be extended by playing it in reverse. This game is quite popular with infants, as it ties in with their interest in playing house, having parties, etc.

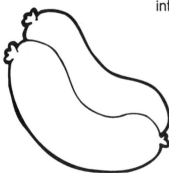

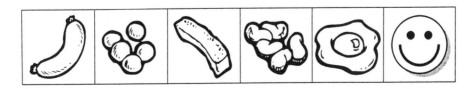

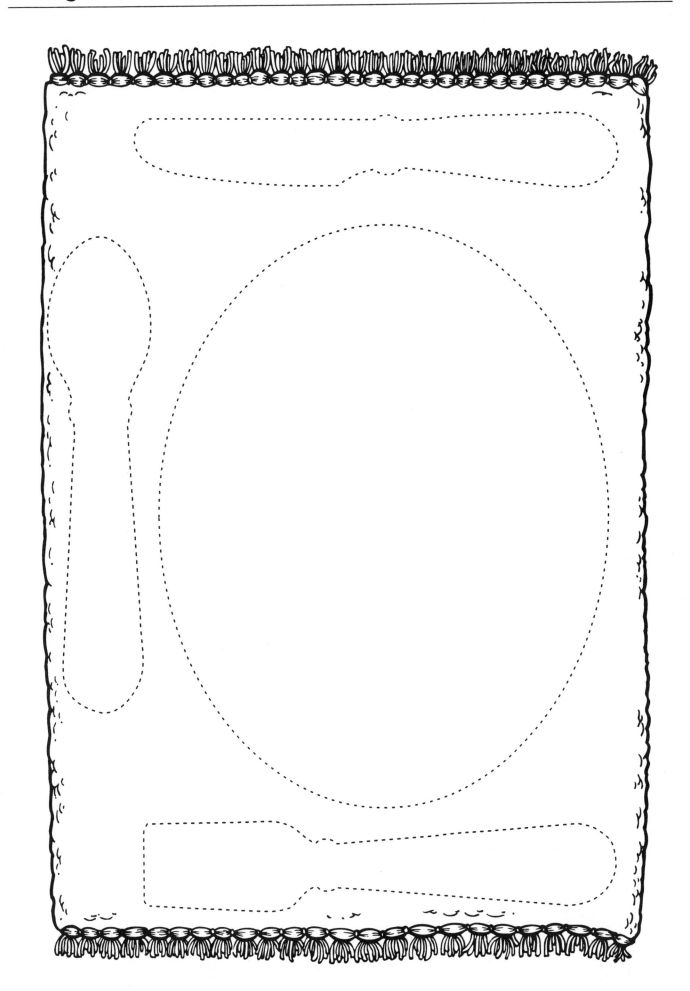

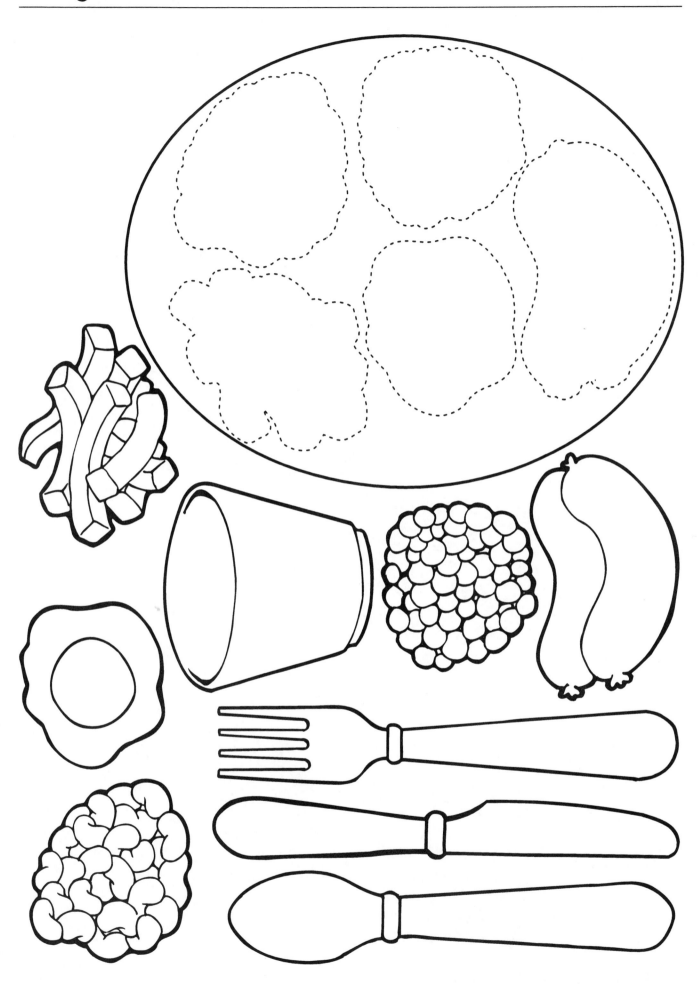

Game 12	Baker's Shop – Toy Shop	Pre-number

Aim:
i) To reinforce the concept of classification and sorting into sets.
ii) To improve memory skills.

What you need:
Two 'Shop' baseboards.

A 'Baker's Shop' sign and a 'Toy Shop' sign.

Ten cards depicting goods belonging in a baker's shop and ten cards depicting goods belonging in a toy shop.

No. of players:
Two.

How to play:
Before play commences, discuss what items are found in a baker's shop and what items belong in a toy shop. Each player selects a baseboard to play on. The cards are shuffled and spread out face down on the table, without overlapping, so they may be picked up easily. Players take turns in selecting a card. If the card belongs to his/her baseboard, they can keep it. If the card does not correspond to the player's baseboard it is placed onto a discard pile. When all of the cards have been picked up, the discard pile is shuffled and spread out face down again as before. Play continues until one player has filled all the spaces on his/her baseboard.

If each player is left with only one space to fill, the teacher or another child can hide both remaining cards behind his/her back. The player whose turn it is next selects which hand they think is holding the card they need. The outcome of the game can often be decided in this manner.

Play variations:
Classification games can be any theme: fruits/vegetables, at the circus/at the beach, birds/butterflies, cats/dogs, things we eat/wear, things with wheels/ without wheels, etc. You can make up your own classification theme by collecting pictures from magazines and using these in place of the illustrations provided in this package.

If you do make up some more classification baseboards, the children can play a 3-4 player variation of the game. Players select which baseboard they will play on. The cards are shuffled and spread face down on the table in a square or rectangle, without touching or overlapping. Players take turns to select two cards and flip them over so all of the players can see them. If any of the cards belong to the player whose turn it is, he/she can place them on his/her baseboard. Any cards that do not belong to the player's baseboard are returned to their face-down position.

It is up to the other players to try and memorise the positions of cards that belong to their baseboard, so they can flip them when it is their turn. The first player to fill all of the spaces on his or her baseboard is the winner. This game is very challenging as a three or four-player game.

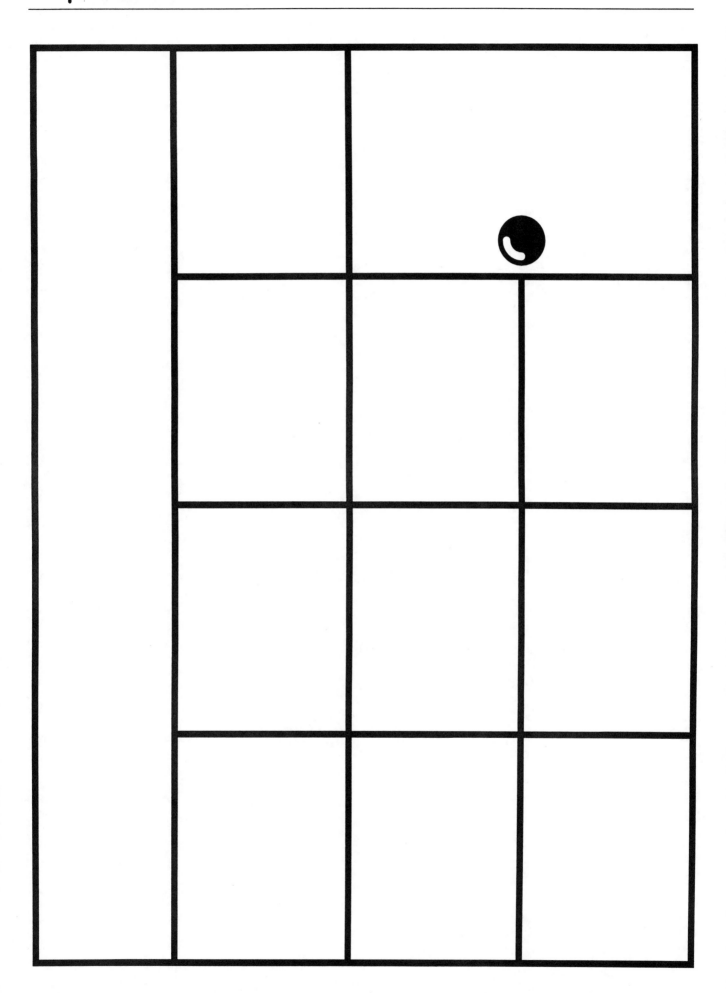

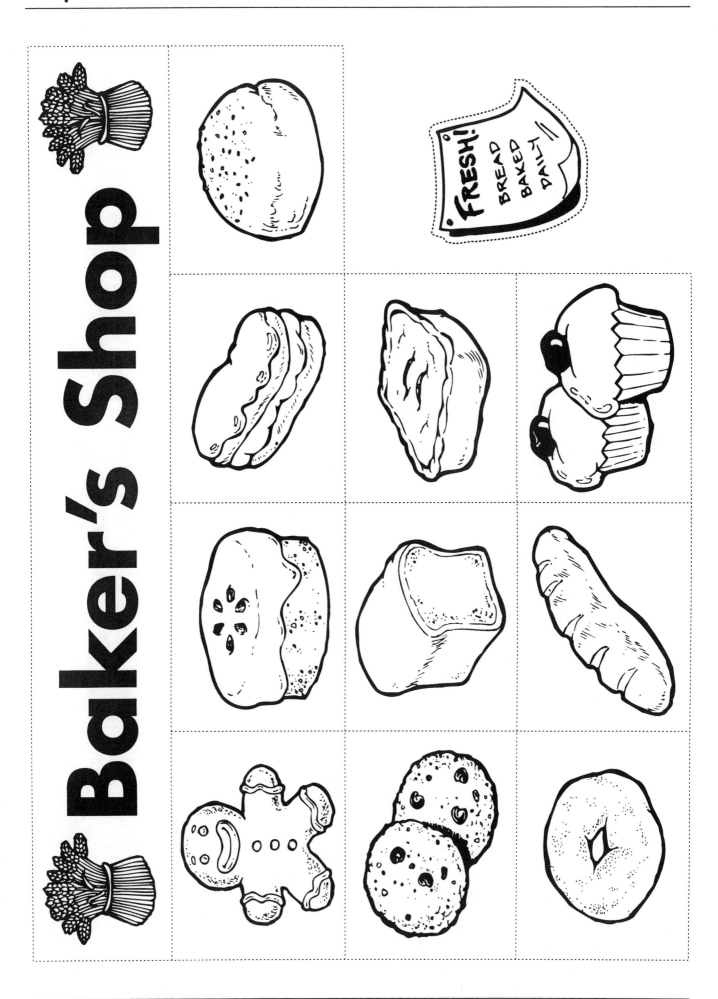

Toy Shop

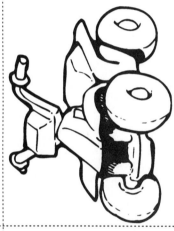

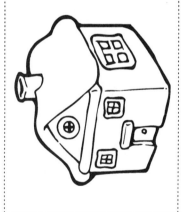

Game 13	Snail	Early Number

Aim:	To reinforce the recognition of the numerals 1 to 10.
What you need:	Two 'Snail' baseboards.
	A ten-sided die. These can be bought from educational and hobby suppliers.
	Twenty two-litre milk container tops, painted. Hobby suppliers stock various nontoxic paints. A nontoxic spray paint could also be used. You could also apply a matt or gloss varnish spray finish to stop the paint from peeling or flaking.
No. of players:	Two.
How to play:	Players take it in turns to throw the die, covering the numerals on the snail's shell with a milk top according to the numeral thrown on the die. The winner is the first player to cover all his/her numerals.

Game 14	Space Invaders	Early Number

Aim:	To reinforce the recognition of the numerals 1 to 10.
What you need:	Two 'Space Invaders' baseboards.
	A ten-sided die. These can be bought from educational and hobby suppliers.
	Twenty two-litre milk container tops, painted. Hobby suppliers stock various nontoxic paints. A nontoxic spray paint could also be used. You could also apply a matt or gloss varnish spray finish to stop the paint from peeling or flaking.
No. of players:	Two.
How to play:	Players take it in turns to throw the die covering each spaceship with a milk top, according to the numeral thrown on the die. The first player to 'zap' all of his/her invading spaceships is the winner.

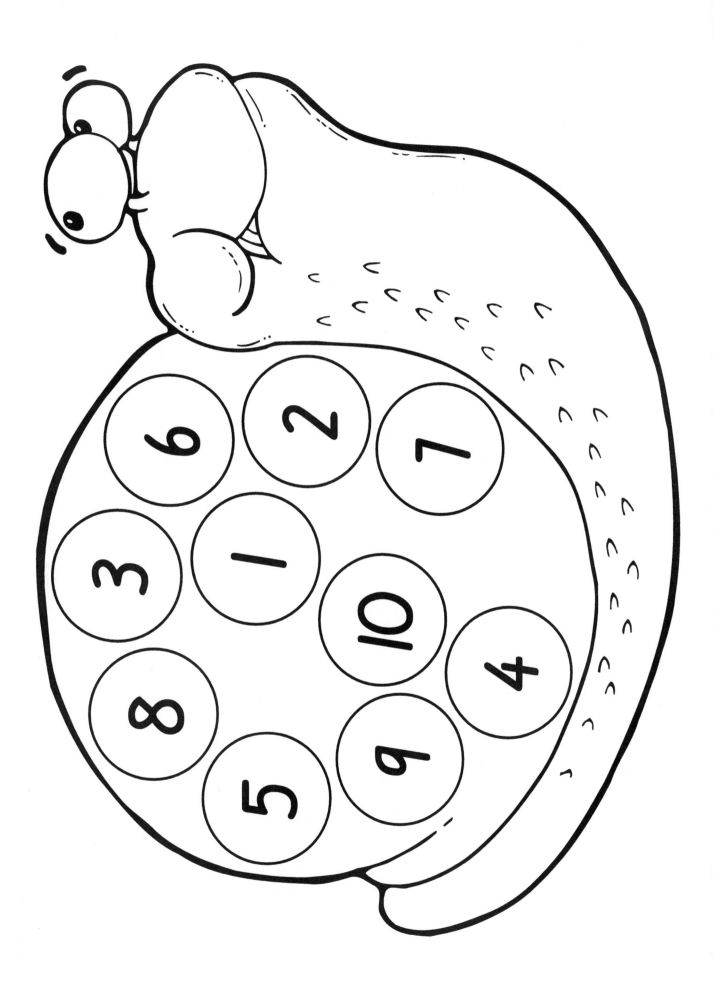

Game 15   Numbered Teddy Bear   Early Number

Aim:	i) To reinforce the recognition of the numerals 1 to 10. ii) To reinforce the recognition of body parts.
What you need:	Two 'Numbered Teddy Bear' baseboards. Two sets of numbered teddy bear body parts. A ten-sided die. These can be bought from educational and hobby suppliers.
No. of players:	Two.
How to play:	Players take it in turns to throw the die, adding the various body parts to their teddy bear, according to the number thrown. The first player to complete his/her teddy bear is the winner. The game can then be extended by playing it in reverse.

Game 16   Birthday Cake   Early Number

Aim:	i) To reinforce the cardinal aspects of the numerals 1 to 6. ii) Introduce the comparison of totals.
What you need:	Two 'Birthday Cake' baseboards. Twelve cardboard candles. These can be made from the artwork provided below. A six-sided die, featuring the numerals 1 to 6.
No. of players:	Two.
How to play:	Players take it in turns to put candles on their baseboard according to their throw of the die. When all the candles have been used the winner is the player with the most candles on their cake. To find out who has the most candles one player matches all of his/her candles with the other player's candles. Alternatively, both players can match their candles on a number line to determine who has the most. This matching on the number line is a physical representation of counting.

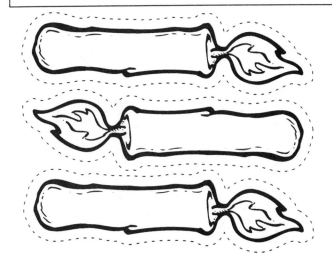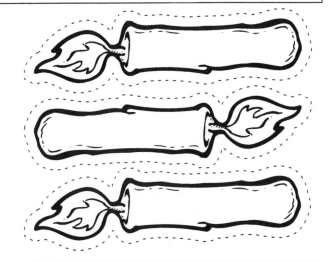

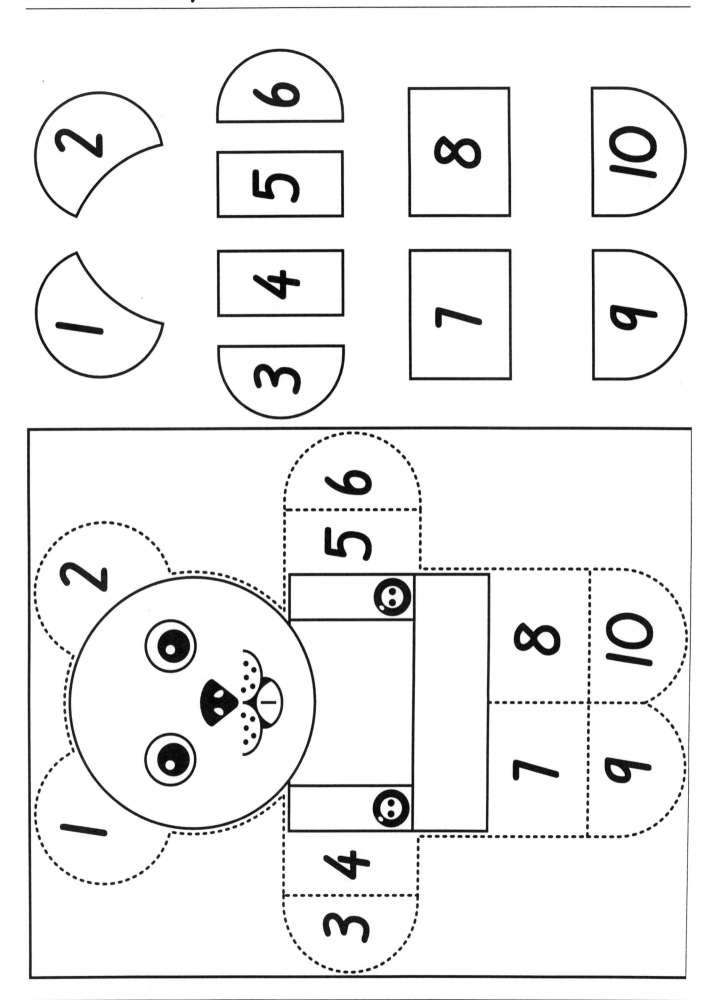

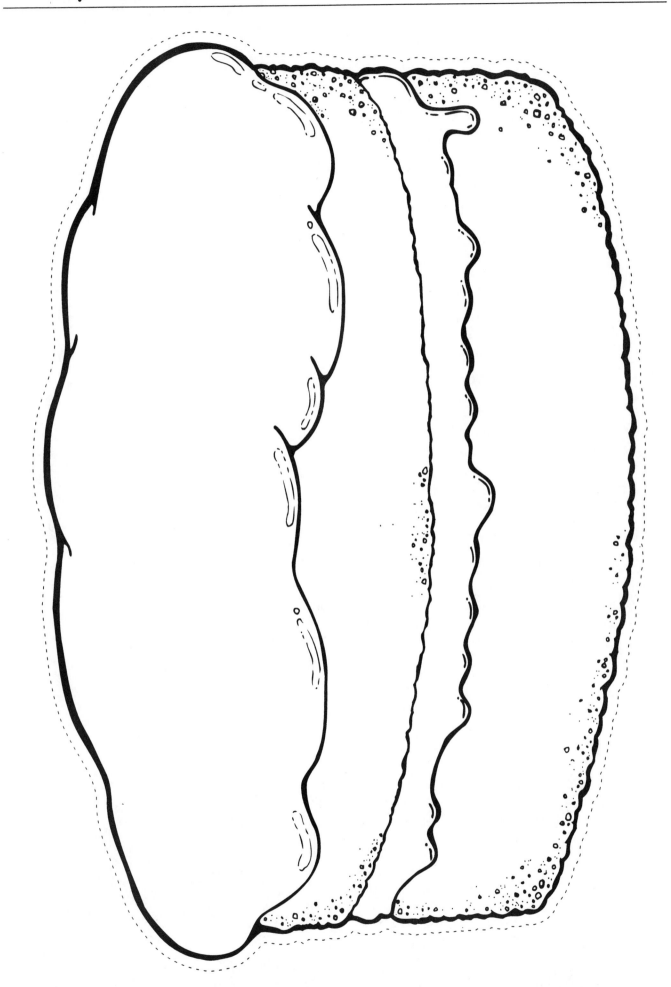

Game 17	Apple Tree	Early Number

Aim:	i) To reinforce the cardinal aspects of the numbers 0 to 5 or 1 to 6.
	ii) To introduce the comparison of totals.
What you need:	Two 'Apple Tree' baseboards.
	A pile of red counters.
	A six-sided die, featuring the numerals 0 to 5 or 1 to 6.
No. of players:	Two.
How to play:	Players take it in turns to throw the die and put apples on their tree according to the number rolled. Play continues until all of the counters have been used up. The winner is the player with the most 'apples' on his/her tree. To discover who has the most apples one player matches their counters with the other player's counters. Alternatively, players can match their counters with a counting strip or number line. This matching is a physical representation of counting. The game may also be extended by playing it in reverse. The winner is the first player to remove all of his/her counters.

Game 18	Frog	Early Number

Aim:	i) To reinforce the cardinal aspects of the numerals 0 to 5 or 1 to 6.
	ii) To introduce the comparison of totals.
What you need:	Two 'Frog' baseboards.
	A pile of yellow counters.
	A six-sided die, featuring the numerals 0 to 5 or 1 to 6.
How to play:	Players take it in turns to throw the die and put 'spots' on their frog according to the number rolled. Play continues until all of the counters have been used up. The winner is the player with the most 'spots' on his/her frog. To discover who has the most 'spots' one player matches their counters with the other player's counters. Alternatively, players can match their counters with a counting strip or number line. This matching is a physical representation of counting. The game may also be extended by playing it in reverse. The winner is the first player to remove all of his/her counters.

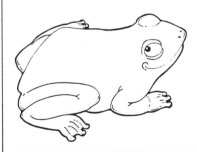

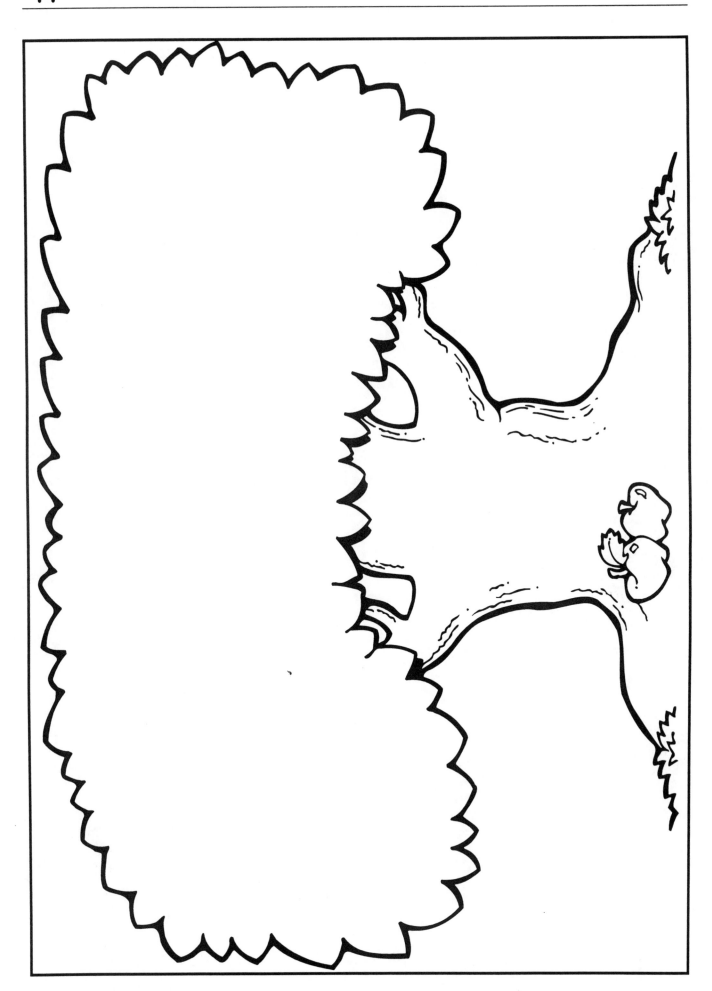

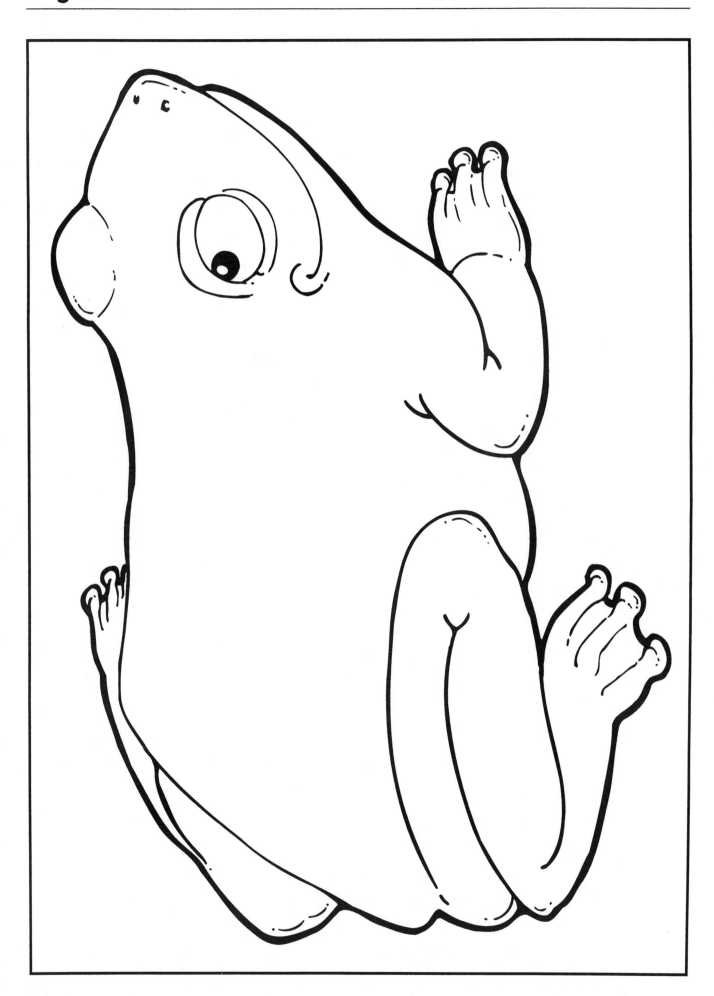

Game 19	The Princess and the Pea	Early Number

Aim: To reinforce the concept of ordering numerals **vertically** from 1 to 5.

What you need: Two 'Princess and the Pea' baseboards.

Two sets of game pieces – ten mattresses in total, numbered 1 to 5 and in a variety of colours.

A six-sided die featuring the numerals 0 to 5.

No. of players: Two.

How to play: Players take it in turns to throw the die. A player must roll a one to start. When a one is rolled, the player can place the first mattress on their baseboard. Then the player must roll a two in order to place the second mattress and so on. The winner is the first player to place all five mattresses on their baseboard. The game may then be extended by playing it in reverse. This time the winner is the first person to take all five mattresses from his/her baseboard.

Game 20	Truck	Early Number

Aim: To reinforce the concept of ordering numerals **horizontally** from 1 to 5.

What you need: Two 'Truck' baseboards.

Two sets of game pieces – five truck parts per player, numbered 1 to 5.

A six-sided die featuring the numbers 0 to 5.

No. of players: Two.

How to play: Players take it in turns to throw the die. A player must roll a one to start. When a one is rolled, the player can place the first part of the truck on their baseboard. Then the player must roll a two in order to place the second part and so on. The winner is the first player to place all five parts on their baseboard. The game may then be extended by playing it in reverse. This time the winner is the first person to remove all five parts from his/her baseboard.

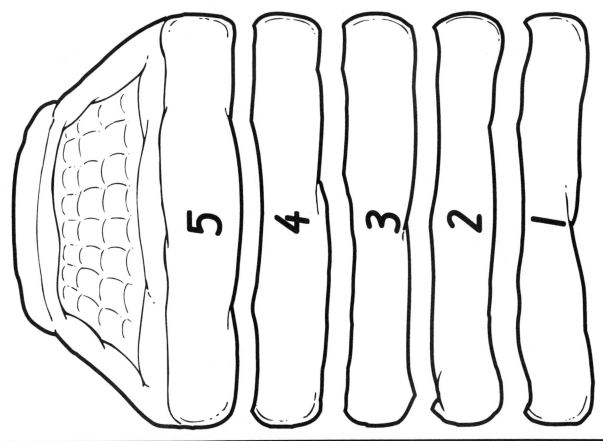

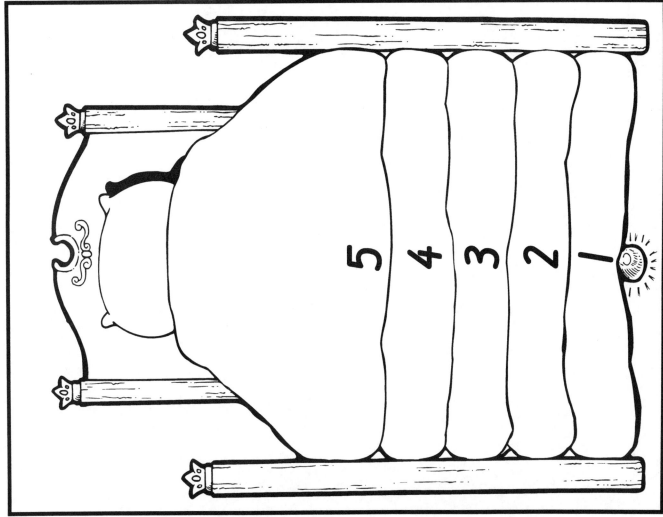

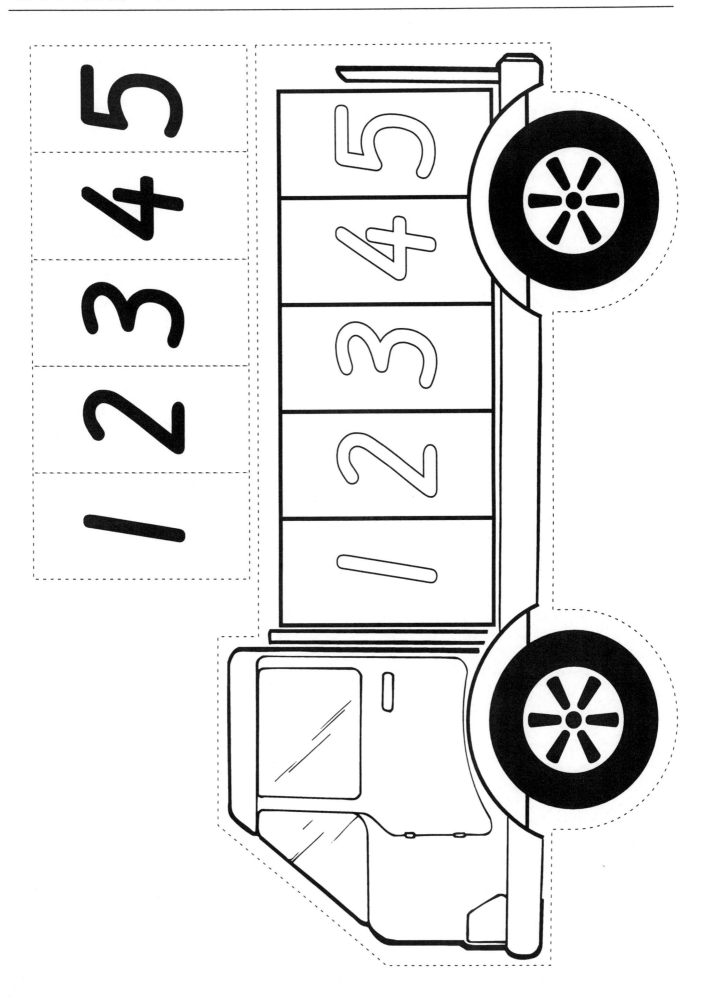

Aim:
  i) To reinforce the cardinal aspects of the numbers 1 to 6 and the partition of the numbers 1 to 6.
  ii) To integrate with the areas of the curriculum dealing with Spring.

What you need: A 'Nest' baseboard for each player.

Twenty egg game pieces with nothing on one side and a baby bird on the other side.

A six-sided die featuring the numerals 0 to 5 or 1 to 6.

No. of players: Two.

How to play: Players take it in turns to throw the die, putting eggs into the nest according to the number thrown. When the nest is full of eggs they can then be turned over according to the throw of the die to hatch. When all the eggs have been hatched the baby birds are then removed from the nest according to the throw of the die to fly away. The winner is the first player to empty his/her nest.

A throw of the die may be split between laying and hatching, or hatching and flying away. For example, if a player throws a four, and there is only **one** space left for an egg to be laid, the player fills that one space with an egg and 'hatches' three of the eggs already laid.

Note: At the start, this game can be played as three separate games. It is useful to back game pieces with thick cardboard, to allow for easier manipulation by the players.

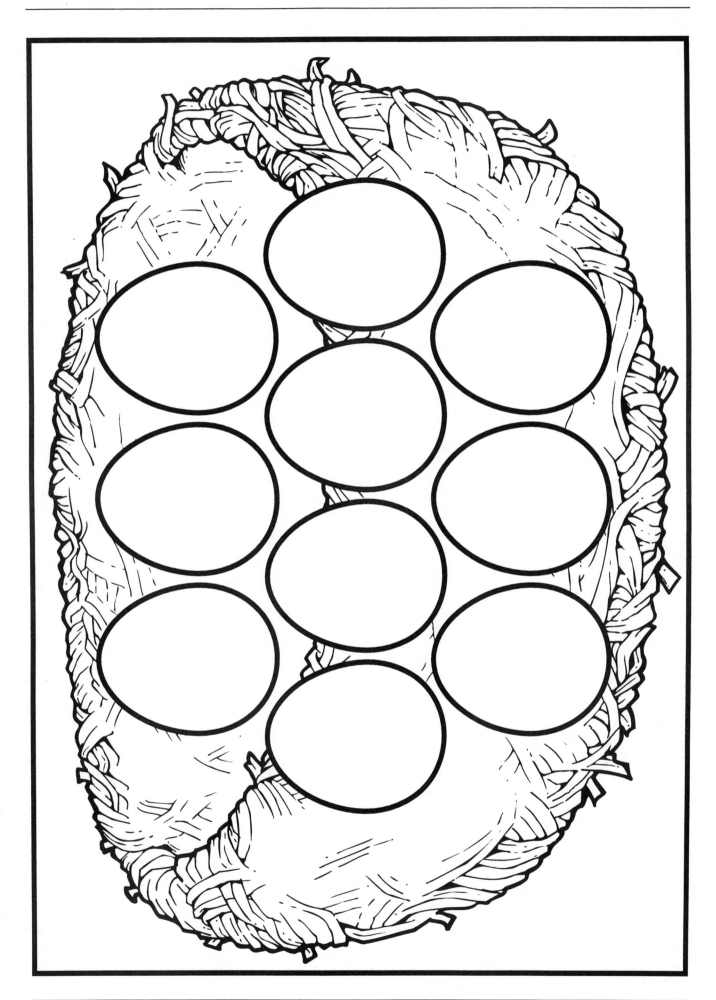

Game 22	Mushroom House	Number

Aim:
i) To reinforce the recognition of numerals 1 to 20 (Level I).
ii) Addition and subtraction skills (Level II).

What you need:
Level I:
A 'Mushroom House' baseboard for each player, 40 counters and a twenty-sided die. These dice are available from educational and hobby outlets.

Level II:
A 'Mushroom House' baseboard and a number strip (1 to 20) for each player, 40 counters and two ten-sided (addition) or two twenty-sided (subtraction) dice.

No. of players:
Two.

How to play:
Level I
Players take it in turns to throw the die. As each number on the roof of the mushroom house is rolled, the player covers it with a counter. Each player may roll two twenty-sided dice instead of one, to speed up the game. The first player to cover all the numerals on his/her baseboard is the winner.

Level II
This variation of the game can be played to reinforce addition or subtraction skills.

For the addition game, use two ten-sided dice. Each player rolls the dice and uses their counting strip to add the two numbers rolled. They then place a counter on the number on their baseboard corresponding to this sum. The first player to cover all the numerals on their baseboard is the winner.

For the subtraction game, use two twenty-sided dice. A counter is placed on the number 20 on both players' baseboards before play starts. Each player rolls the dice, then subtracts the smaller number from the larger number, using their counting strip as an aid for counting back. They then cover the corresponding number on their baseboard. The first player to cover all the numerals on their baseboard is the winner.

The Level II game variations have a high level of difficulty for this age group. Throughout the various classroom activities involving addition, make a clear distinction between 'putting together', which refers to sets and objects, and 'adding', which refers to numerals.

1	2	3	4	5	6	7	8	9	10	glue halves together here

11	12	13	14	15	16	17	18	19	20

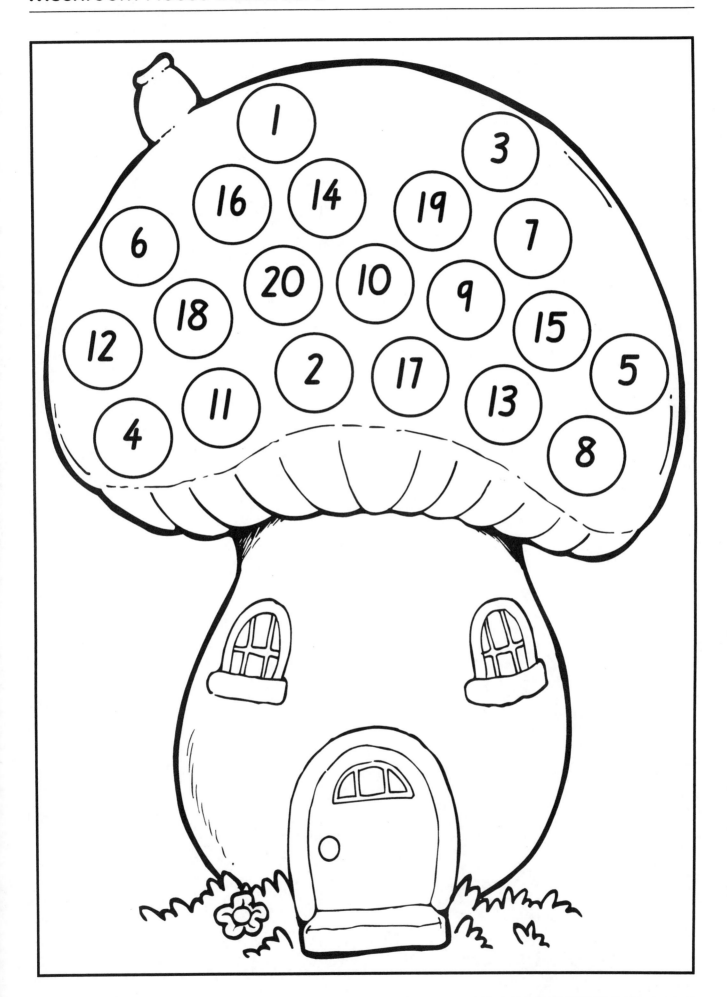

Game 23	Spaceship/Train	Number

Aim:
To give practice in counting on and counting back, leading to an understanding of the number line and applying this idea to the concept of addition and subtraction. This game can be adapted to the ability and interests of the players in various ways.

What you need:
For the spaceship game (Level I):
A 'Spaceship' baseboard, four ladder baseboards (making twenty rungs in total), a six-sided die featuring the numerals 0 to 5 and a marker to move up and down the ladder for each game player. You can use the markers provided or make your own.

For the trains game (Level II):
Two 'Train' baseboards, four ladder baseboards (making twenty rungs in total), a six-sided die featuring the numerals 0 to 5 and one marker, which is shared between two players.

For the spaceship game variation (Level III):
A 'Spaceship' baseboard, four ladder baseboards (making twenty rungs in total), a pack of twenty cards with movement instructions given on them and a marker and cargo container for each player. The instruction cards are supplied on page 42.

No. of players:
Two or three.

How to play:
Level I
Each player takes turns to throw the die and move their marker up the ladder according to the number thrown. The first player to reach the spaceship at the top of the ladder is the winner. They can then have a race to see who will reach the bottom of the ladder first.

Level II
This two-player game variation uses the ladder pieces as a train track. A train is placed at each end of the track, facing in different directions. Each player chooses a train they wish to travel to. The players place a marker which they share in the middle of the track, between rung 10 and 11. The players then take turns to roll the die and move the marker along the track towards their train according to the number they roll. The winner is the first player to get the marker onto his/her train.

Level III
This variation of the spaceship game uses instruction cards instead of a die to determine the players movement. The baseboards are set up as for the spaceship game. The pack of twenty cards is shuffled and placed face down in a pile centrally between the players. Players then take turns to take a card from the pile and move their marker up and down the ladder according to the instructions on the cards. As the cards are used, they are placed into a new pile. If all twenty cards are used, they are reshuffled and play continues. The first player to reach the top of the ladder, take his/her cargo and climb back down is the winner.

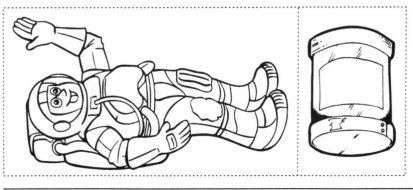

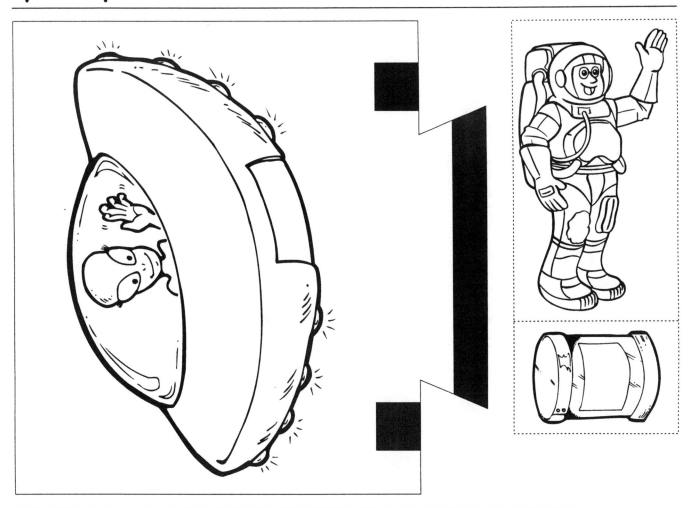

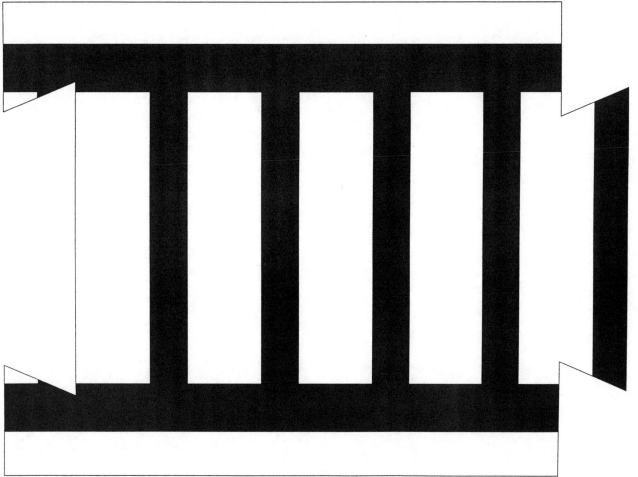

Move forward one space.	Move forward two spaces.	Move forward three spaces.
Move forward four spaces.	Move backward one space.	Move backward two spaces.
Move backward three spaces.	Move forward five spaces.	Move backward four spaces.
Move behind previous player.	Move in front of previous player.	Move forward one space.
Move in front of next player.	Move behind next player.	Move forward two spaces.
Move forward three spaces.	Move backward one space.	Move backward two spaces.

Game 24   House   Number

Aim: To consolidate understanding of number bonds from 5 to 10.

What you need: A 'House' baseboard for each player.

Two sets of cards featuring a 'door number' and a set of number bond cards corresponding to this number. For example, the number bonds for the number 6 are 5+1, 0+6, 3+3, 4+2, 3+2+1, and so on. You can use the cards supplied on page 46, or make up your own cards, which will allow you to also use subtraction sentences such as 12-6, 10-4 or 6-0.

1-cm cubes for players to check the number bonds.

No. of players: Two.

How to play: Using a removable adhesive, attach a numeral between 5 and 10 onto the door of each player's baseboard. The number bond cards for the numbers chosen are shuffled and placed face down between the players in a pile. Players take turns to turn over the top card. They work out the number bond on the card, using 1-cm cubes if necessary. If the answer is the same as the number on the front door of their house, they get to keep the card, and place it in one of the window spaces on their house. If the answer is not the one on their house door, the card is placed in a discard pile. When all of the number bond cards have been used, the discard pile is shuffled and placed face down in a pile again and the game continues. The winner is the first player to collect all the number bonds for his/her target number.

Start players on the number bonds for 5 and 6 and move on to 7, 8, 9 and 10 as player skill improves. This game can be played by two or more players. Include a target number and its number bond card set for each player.

Use these blank cards to make up your own number bond sets.

5	6	7	8	

5 + 0	4 + 1	3 + 2	5 - 0
2+2+1	1+3+1	6 - 1	7 - 2
6 + 0	5 + 1	4 + 2	6 - 0
3 + 3	1+2+3	2+2+2	7 - 1
7 + 0	6 + 1	5 + 2	4 + 3
4+2+1	3+3+1	3+2+2	7 - 0
8 + 0	7 + 1	6 + 2	5 + 3
4 + 4	4+3+1	3+3+2	5+2+1

Game 25	Hen	Number

Aim:	To consolidate understanding of number bonds for the numerals 1 to 10.
What you need:	A 'Hen' baseboard for each player.
	Twenty 'egg' counters.
	A ten-sided die.
No. of players:	Two.
How to play:	Players take it in turns to throw the die. They compare the number thrown to the number bonds on their baseboard. If they find a number bond that matches the number thrown they may place an 'egg' counter on that number bond. Play continues until one player has covered all of his/her eggs. The first player to do this is the winner.

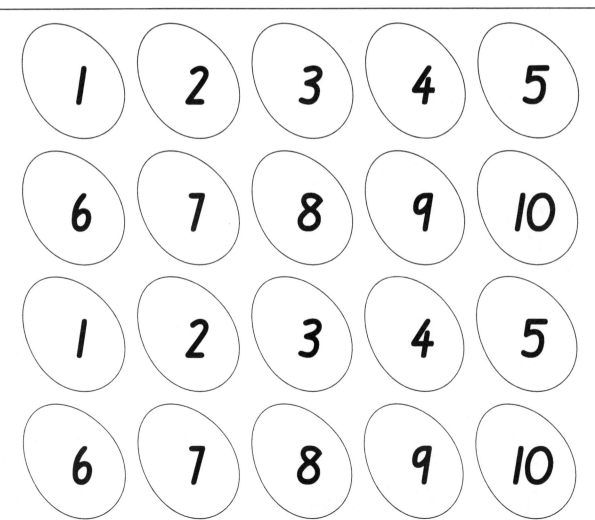

Use these eggs as markers for the baseboard.

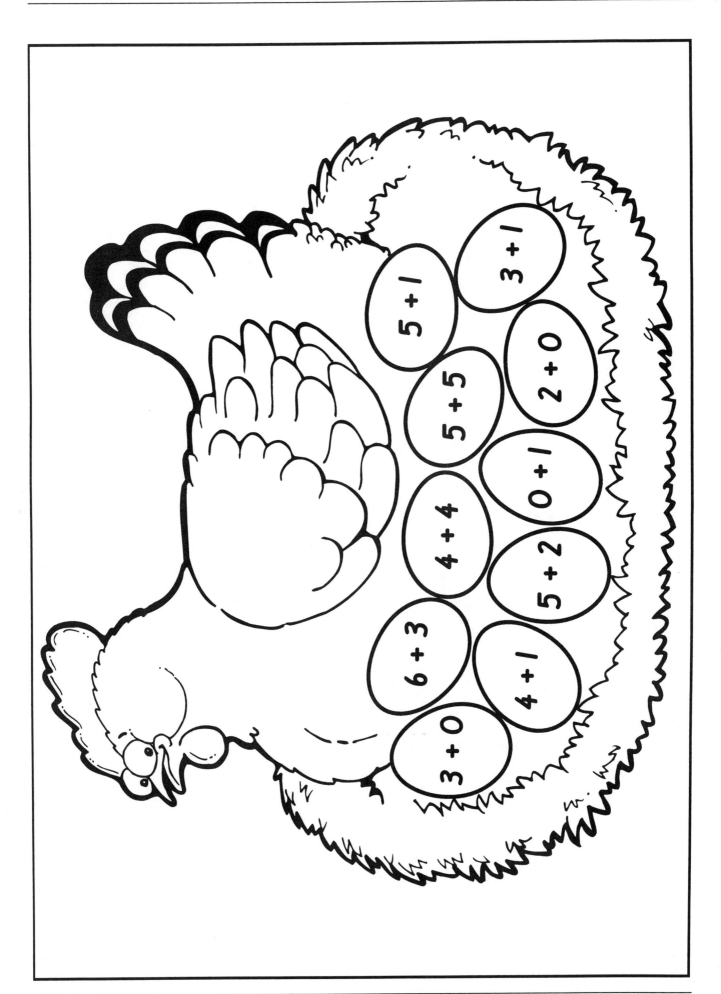

Game 26	The Racetrack	Number

Aim:
    i) To practise moving from one space to the next using a counter.
    ii) To practise counting on.
    iii) To practise addition skills.

What you need:
Six racetrack side baseboards and four racetrack corner baseboards, arranged into a racetrack like this:

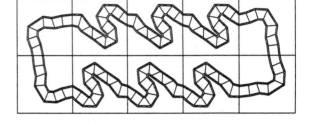

One or two six-sided dice featuring the numerals 1 to 6.

A place marker for each player.

No. of players:
Two to six.

How to play:
Set up the baseboards as described above. You could also construct longer or shorter tracks by using more or less baseboards.

Players take turns to throw the die. Players move their marker around the track according to the number thrown. The first player to finish a complete circuit of the track is the winner.

As a variation of this game, players could use two dice instead of one, adding together the numbers thrown and moving their marker that number of spaces.

Some other variations you could add to make the game more exciting are:

- Introduce bonuses and hazards along the way by adding symbols to some of the board squares and making up rules associated with these. For example, landing on a smiley face symbol might mean the player gets to move forward an extra space. Other symbols might signify an extra roll of the dice, or a chance to draw a card which may give other bonuses or a penalty. Cards may incorporate a question which has to be answered correctly to receive the bonus.

- Have one player chase another as in a cat and mouse game. Have safe areas along the way where the mouse can 'rest'. If the cat lands on a safe area it misses a turn.

- Call the game 'Jungle Journey'. Paste pictures of jungle animals randomly along the track. The animals must be appeased before the players can progress past them. For example, players have to feed the lion two pieces of meat before they can pass. Players could collect these items along the way by landing on special squares.

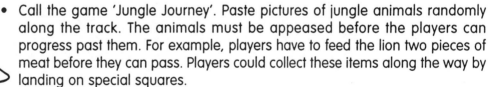

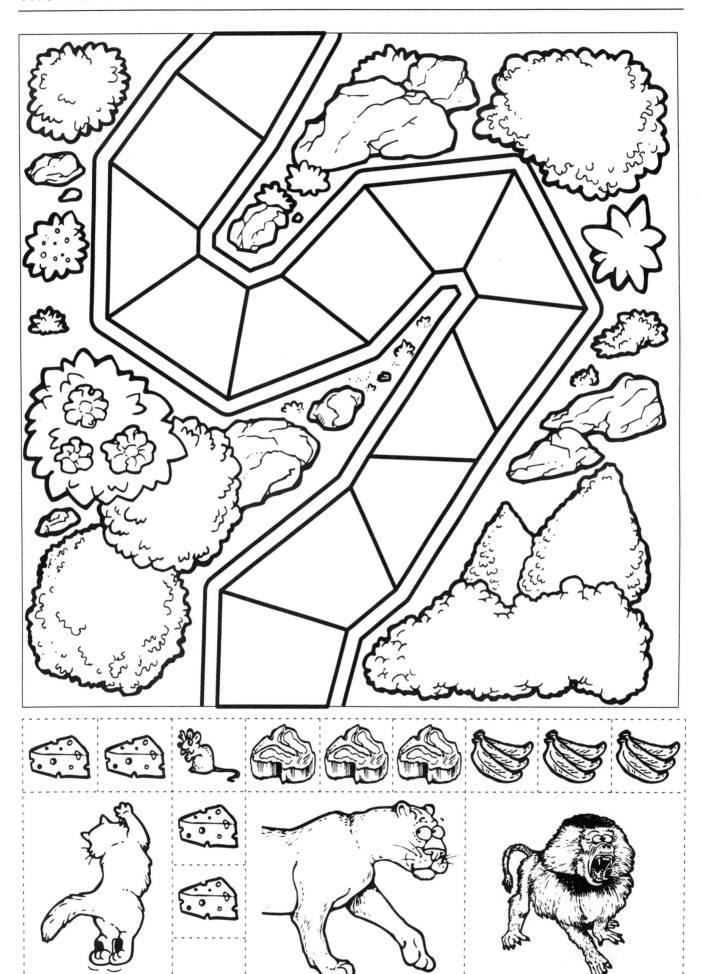

Game 27 — The Longest Train — Measurement

Aim:	i) To reinforce the concept of long, longer, longest, short, shorter, shortest.
	ii) To reinforce left–right orientation.
What you need:	A train engine and ten carriages per player.
	A six-sided die with the numerals 1 to 3 only (repeat each number on two sides). Alternatively, you could use three beans painted on one side. Players add 1 to 3 carriages per turn with the number of carriages being determined by the number of beans which land coloured side up.
	For older children, use a six-sided die featuring the numbers 0 to 5 or 1 to 6.
No. of players:	Two or three.
How to play:	Players place their engines one below each other at the far left side of the play area. They take it in turns to throw the die or beans, adding on carriages to their engine according to the number thrown. As play progresses the children can see whose train is longer, shorter or equal in length. Play is over when all of the carriages have been used up. The winner is the player who has the longest train.

Game 28 — The Longest Snake — Measurement

Aim:	To reinforce the concept of long, longer, longest, short, shorter, shortest.
What you need:	A snake head, tail and ten body lengths per player.
	A six-sided die with the numerals 1 to 3 only (repeat each number on two sides). Alternatively, you could use three beans painted on one side. Players add 1 to 3 body lengths per turn with the number of body lengths being determined by the number of beans which land coloured side up.
	For older children, use a six-sided die featuring the numbers 0 to 5 or 1 to 6.
No. of players:	Up to three.
How to play:	Players place their snake head cards one under the other at the far left of the area of play. They take it in turns to throw the die or beans, adding on body lengths according to the number thrown, making sure that all the body parts are placed end-to-end without any gaps. As play progresses children can see whose snake is longer, shorter or the same. Play is over when all the snake body parts have been used up and the winner is the player who has the longest snake.

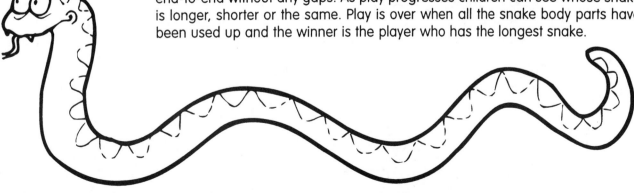

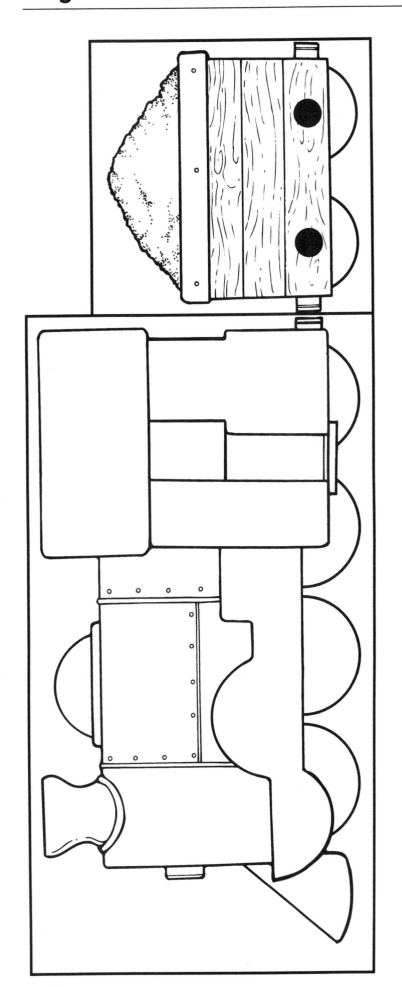

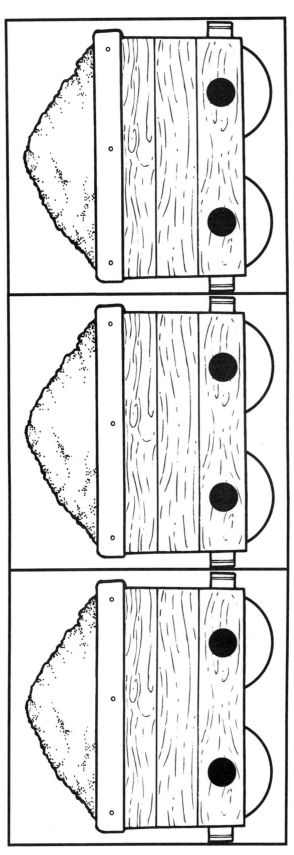

Make up a total of ten carriages for each train.

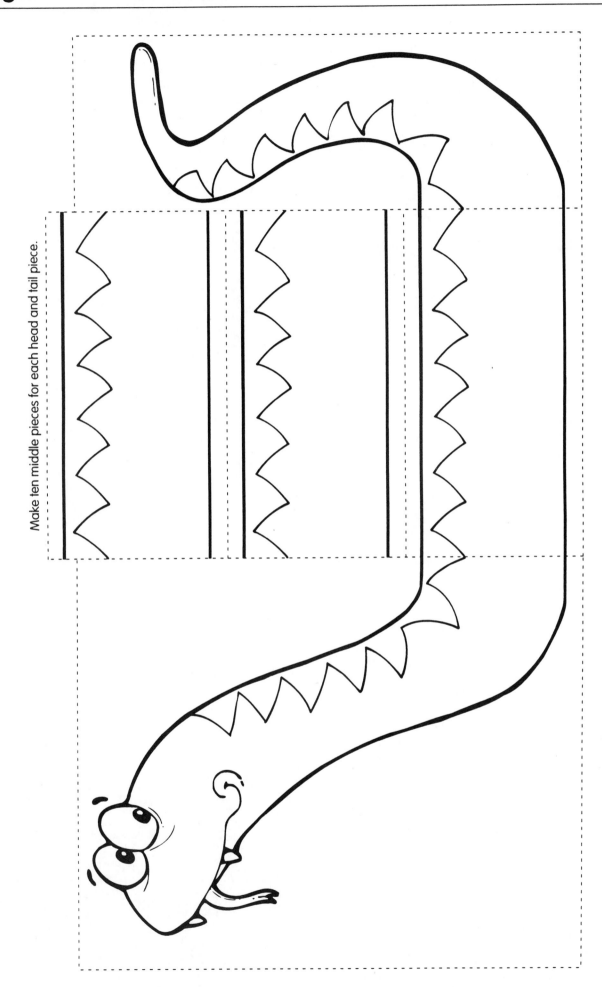

Make ten middle pieces for each head and tail piece.

Game 29	The Tallest Sunflower	Measurement

Aim:	To reinforce the concept of tall, taller, tallest.
What you need:	A sunflower card and ten stem cards per player.
	A six-sided die with the numerals 1 to 3 only (repeat each number on two sides). Alternatively, you could use three beans painted on one side. Players add 1 to 3 stem cards per turn with the number of stem cards being determined by the number of beans which land coloured side up.
No. of players:	Up to three.
How to play:	Players put their sunflower cards side-by-side along the bottom edge of the table. They then take it in turns to throw the die, adding stem pieces to their sunflower according to the number thrown, making sure that all the stem cards are placed end-to-end without gaps. As play continues, players can keep an eye on each other's progress. The game is over when all the stem pieces have been used up. The winner is the child who has the tallest sunflower.

Game 30	Clock	Measurement

Aim:	(i) To teach the 'o'clocks' from 1 to 12 (inclusive).
	(ii) To record special times on the clock face.
What you need:	A 'Clock' baseboard for each player.
	A long stick or straw to represent the long hand on the clock.
	A short stick or straw to represent the short hand on the clock.
	A pile of counters.
	A twelve-sided die.
No. of players:	Two.
How to play:	Players take turns to throw the die and make the corresponding 'o'clock' on the clock face using the long and short sticks. Each time they make an 'o'clock' correctly they cover the relevant number with a counter. The winner is the first player to cover all the numerals on his/her clock face correctly.

Make five left-handed leaves and five right-handed leaves.

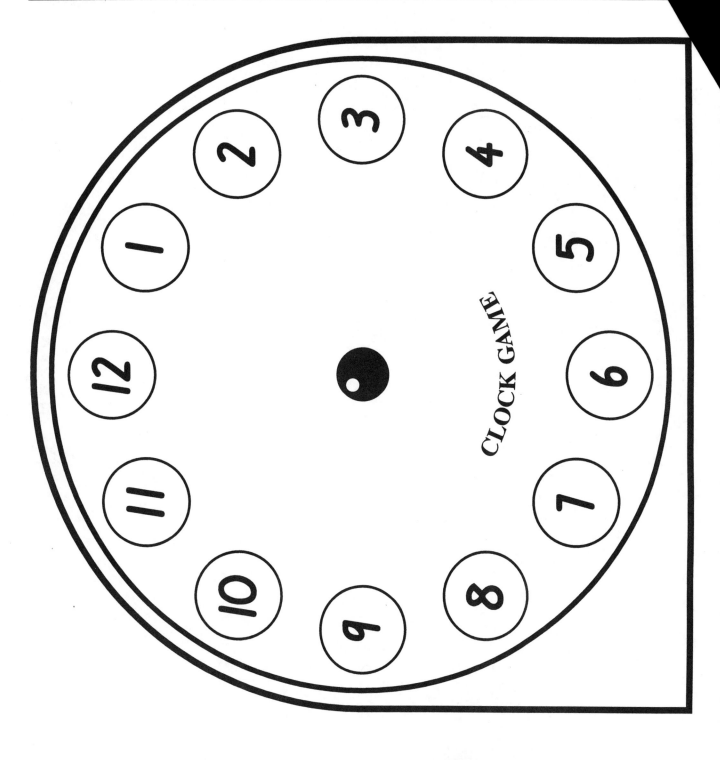

CLOCK GAME

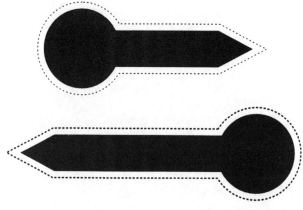